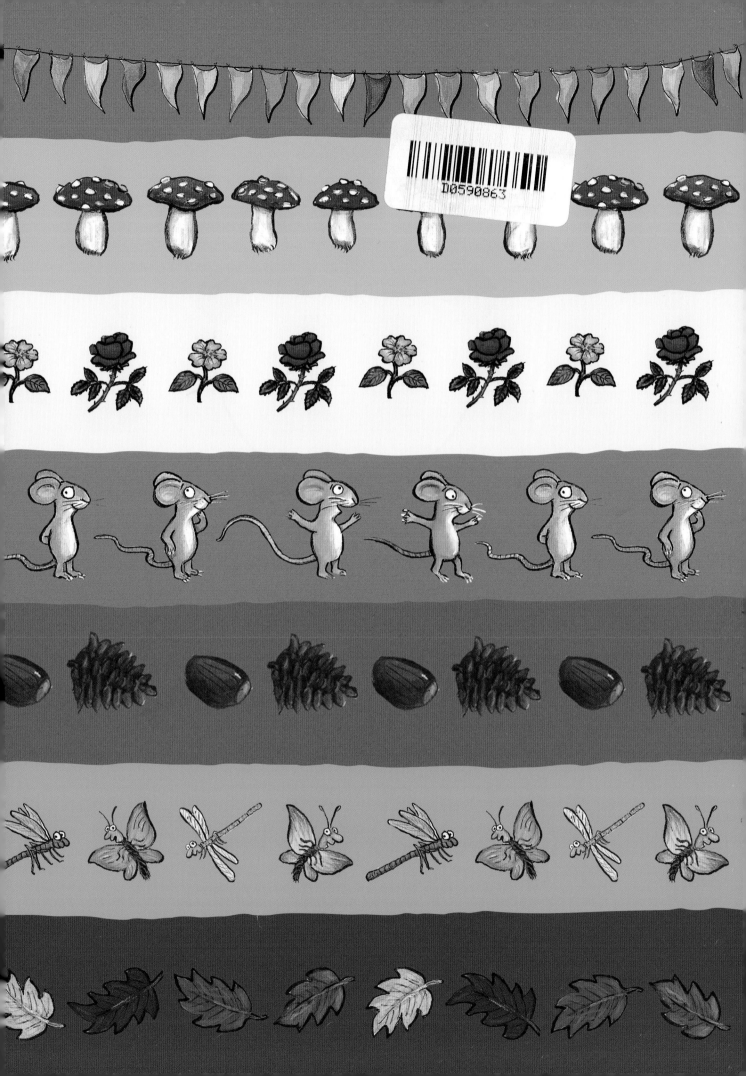

This
Gruffalo Annual
belongs to

_____

First published 2015 by Macmillan Children's Books
an imprint of Pan Macmillan
20 New Wharf Road, London N1 9RR
Associated companies throughout the world
www.panmacmillan.com

ISBN: 978-1-509-80133-6

Based on the bestselling picture books *The Gruffalo* and *The Gruffalo's Child*
by Julia Donaldson and Axel Scheffler

Editorial: Amanda Li
Design: Dan Newman
Photography: Stuart Cox
Photography on Creating the Gruffalo: Eliz Hüseyin
Portrait of Julia Donaldson on page 40: Steve Ullathorne

1 3 5 7 9 8 6 4 2

A CIP catalogue record for this book is available from the British Library.

Printed in Italy

Contents

The Gruffalo and Me

The Gruffalo

Me

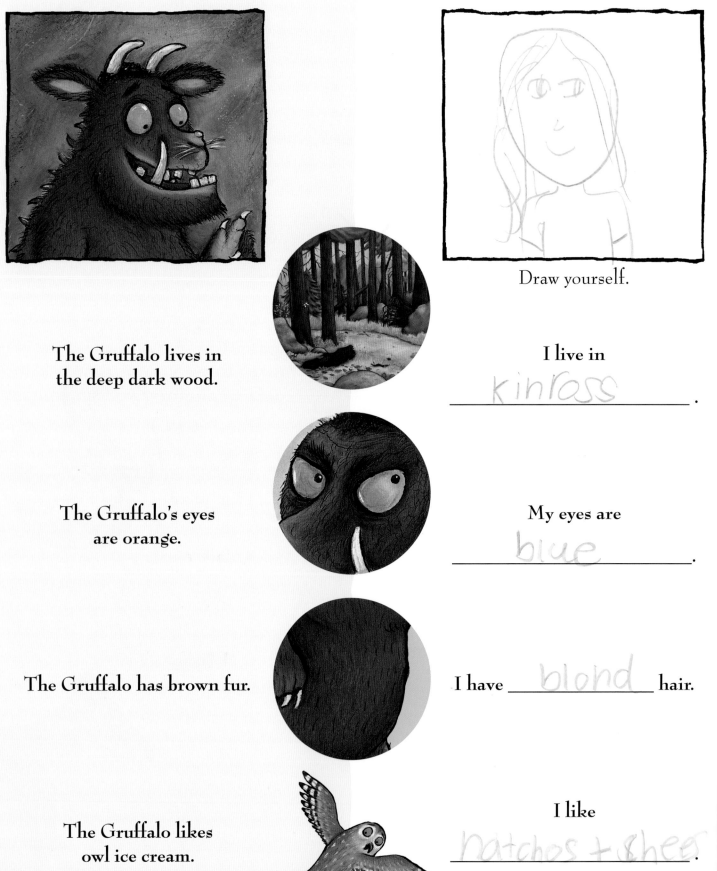

Draw yourself.

The Gruffalo lives in the deep dark wood.

I live in

kinross .

The Gruffalo's eyes are orange.

My eyes are

blue .

The Gruffalo has brown fur.

I have _blond_ hair.

The Gruffalo likes owl ice cream.

I like

natchos + sheg .

What Do You Like?

The Gruffalo's Child likes:

- Listening to stories
- Drawing pictures
- Her toys
- Exploring the woods
- Her cosy cave
- The Gruffalo!

What do you like? Make a list:

- ....
- ....
- ....
- ....
- ....
- ....

Take Your Pick!

Which of the two would you rather do?
You have to choose one. Just tick the box.

Would you rather . . .

☐ make friends with a Gruffalo?
or
☐ make friends with a Big Bad Mouse?

Would you rather . . .

☐ have knobbly knees?
or
☐ have purple prickles?

Would you rather . . .

☐ drink Gruffalo tea?
or
☐ eat Gruffalo cake?

Would you rather . . .

☐ live in a cave like a Gruffalo?
or
☐ live in a treetop house like an owl?

Would you rather . . .

☐ eat roasted fox?
or
☐ eat scrambled snake?

Would you rather . . .

☐ fly like an owl?
or
☐ slither like a snake?

What's Gone from the Gruffalo?

The Gruffalo is missing lots of body parts.
Can you help him?

Draw his:

- tusk ✓
- ears ✓
- horns ✓
- tail ✓
- prickles ✓
- eyebrows ✓
- whiskers ✓
- missing claws ✓
- knobbly knees ✓

What a funny-looking Gruffalo!

A is for Acorn

Have you ever picked up an acorn? It is a small, green-brown nut in a tiny case. The case looks like a little hat. An acorn falls from an oak tree and if one takes root in the ground, it will begin to grow … and grow … One day, that tiny acorn could itself become an enormous oak tree.

B is for Butterfly

Sometimes butterflies flutter by in the deep dark wood. You can't miss their colourful wings.

A butterfly starts life as a caterpillar, which hatches out of a tiny egg. Once the caterpillar has grown, it forms a hard case around itself called a chrysalis. After some time, a lovely butterfly breaks out of the chrysalis. Beautiful!

C is for Conker

In the autumn it's fun to collect conkers that have fallen on to the ground. Some conkers are still in their prickly green cases, so be careful of your fingers. Other cases split open, showing the shiny brown conker – or horse chestnut – inside. There are lots of things you can do with conkers. Who can find the biggest one?

D is for Dragonfly

With its long, thin body and delicate, transparent wings, a dragonfly likes to hove near water. But you'll have to be quick to sp one, as it is one of the fastest flying insects. Dragonflies can even fly backwards!

the Deep Dark Wood

E is for Earth

All the plants in the deep dark wood need earth to grow in. Do you know what earth is made from? Tiny bits of rock, water, air, dead plants, dead animals – and worm poo. Earthworms live in the soil and feed on all the dead bits of plant and animal, keeping the earth healthy. Look out for worm casts – little curly piles of earth that have passed through a worm.

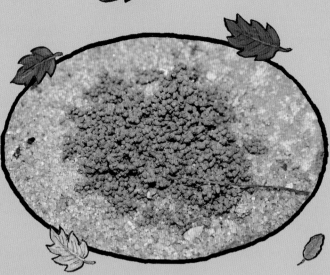

F is for Footprint

It's fun to make footprints in sticky, squelchy mud or in crunchy, white snow.

Creatures like dogs, foxes, rabbits and birds often leave interesting tracks behind them.

G is for Grow

Look around you the next time you go for a walk in the woods. Almost everything you can see is growing, very, very slowly. It can take years for seeds to grow into trees and bushes.

All plants need water, sunlight and air to grow well – just like you!

Answers on page 61!

A Walk in the Woods

Follow the path through the deep dark wood and complete the tasks.

1. Who's looking out of the tree? Draw the creature.

1

2

2. Here's the snake's logpile house. How many logs are there? Count them and write the number.

3

3. Look! Footprints ...
Do they belong to a:

Mouse? ☐

Gruffalo? ☐

Fox? ☐

7. Sssh! The Gruffalo and his Child are asleep in their cave. Draw the Gruffalo's Child a toy to play with when she wakes up.

You made it! Have a nice rest.

6. A butterfly is flying past. Can you draw a lovely pattern on its wings?

5. How many pine cones are on the path? Write the number.

4. Watch out for the stream! Draw stepping stones to cross it.

Make a Mini
Shadow Puppet Theatre

Let's put on a Gruffalo shadow puppet show!

You will need:

- a sheet of tracing paper
- a large sheet of tissue paper
- a pencil
- an empty cereal box
- scissors
- two straws or clean lolly sticks
- glue or sticky tape
- a torch or desk lamp
- a grown-up helper

! Ask a grown-up to help with the tricky cutting.

1. First, cut out the back of the cereal box.

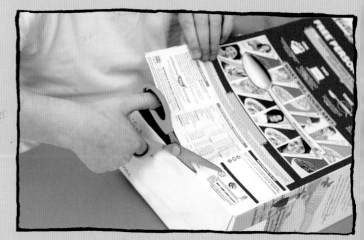

2. Then glue or tape the corners of the remaining box to make a strong frame.
3. Trace these shapes of the Gruffalo and the mouse on to the tracing paper.
4. Glue the tracing paper on to the piece of card left over from the back of the cereal box.

5. Then cut out a large rectangle from the other side of the box, leaving a 2cm frame around the edge.

6. Cut a piece of tissue paper to fit inside the frame and glue it in. This is your puppet theatre.

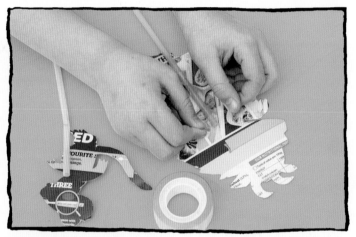

7. When the Gruffalo and the mouse are dry, cut them out very carefully.

8. Tape a straw or lolly stick to the back of each one – like this.

Put the theatre on the edge of a table so that you can kneel or stand behind it.

Place the torch directly behind the theatre so that the light shines brightly through the tissue. Hold the puppets by the straw or stick and make them move around behind the tissue screen.

Ask someone to watch the puppets from the audience side of the theatre and experiment until you get the best shadow effect. You might need to put the torch on a chair behind you for this.

Now make up your own story about the Gruffalo and the mouse. It's up to you!

Snowy Tracks

Aha! Oho! A track in the snow!
Whose is this track and where does it go?

Draw lines to match the tracks to the right animal.

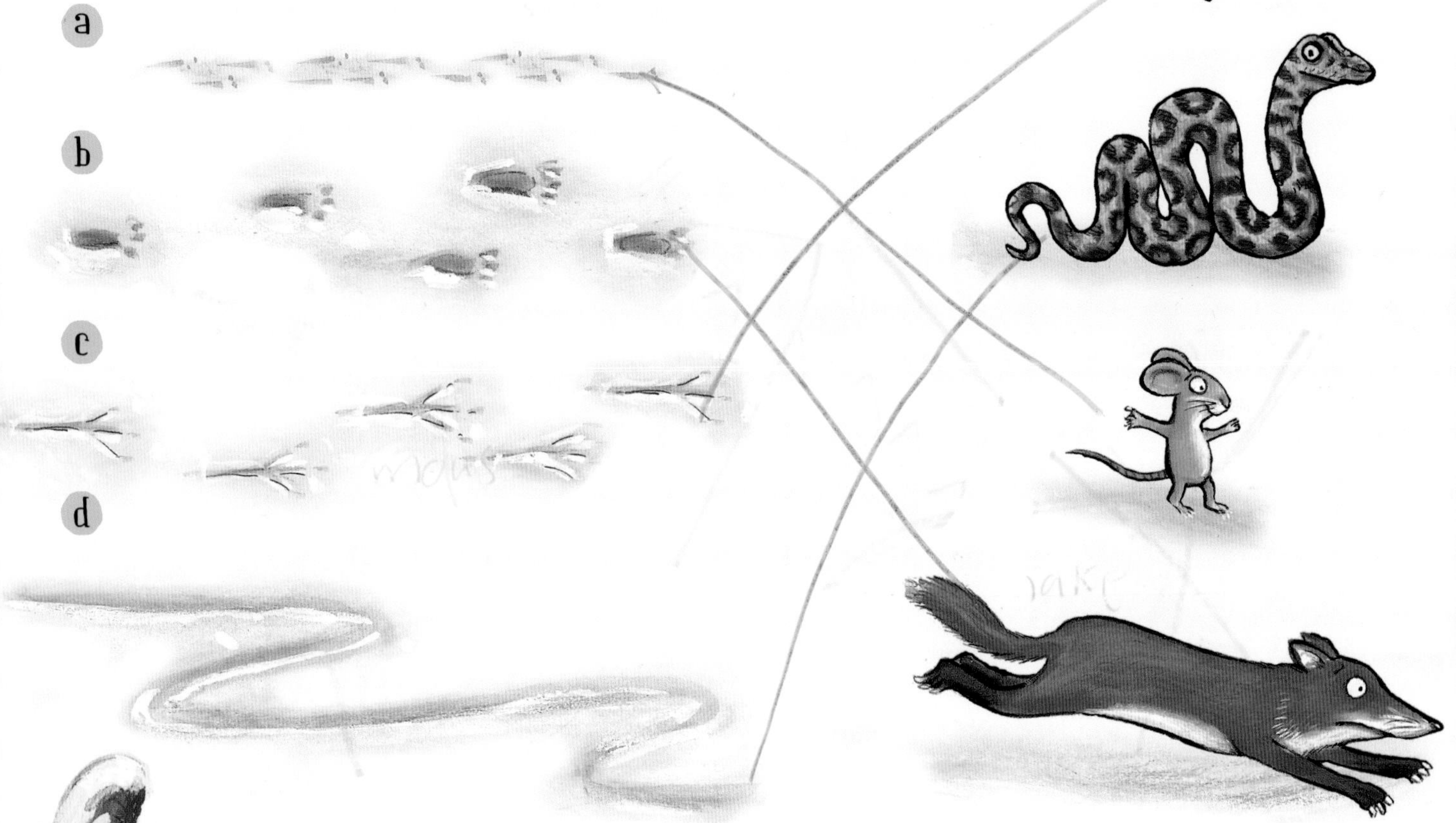

a

b

c

d

Now draw some Gruffalo footprints in the snow.

Things to Know About Snow

Snow is cold, wet – and fun to play in! But where does it come from?

❄ When it's very cold outside, water in the air forms into tiny ice crystals.
The crystals stick together and become snowflakes, which fall to the ground.

❄ Snowflakes can be made up of more than a hundred ice crystals.
Every crystal is different – but they are all beautiful to look at.

❄ Every snowflake has
six sides or branches.

❄ If there is a lot of snow, it settles on the ground like a thick
blanket. That's when the fun begins. You can sledge, build a
snowman or even have a snowball fight!

❄ In cold, snowy weather, animals have to find ways to survive.
Some animals do this by hibernating. This means that they
go to sleep in a cosy place during the long winter months and
wake up when it gets warmer again. Animals that do this
include hedgehogs, dormice, bats, frogs and butterflies.
Would *you* like to sleep through the winter?

A snow joke
What do you call a
snowman in July?
A puddle!

17

Creating the Gruffalo
by Axel Scheffler

There are lots of stages to creating one of my pictures. The first thing I do is make a pencil sketch.

I then draw over the pencil with black ink using a dip pen. I have to keeping dipping the pen into the ink pot.

Now I can start the colouring-in.

I colour the picture using watercolours.

I use my dip pen again to add extra detail, like the texture of the Gruffalo's fur.

Here I am painting the mouse's whiskers with a special, thick paint called gouache.

Finally, I clean the picture by gently rubbing out any pencil lines that are showing.

And here is my finished picture of the Gruffalo and the mouse!

Animal Art

Gruffalos like drawing.
Which animals do you think they have drawn on the cave wall?

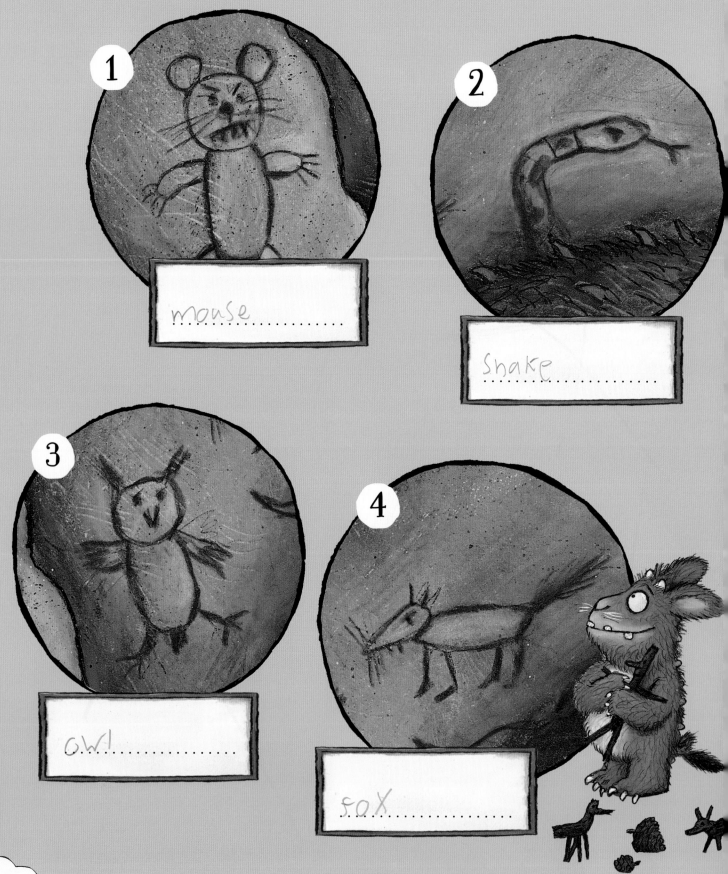

1 mouse

2 snake

3 owl

4 fox

Can you draw animals too?
Draw two of your favourite animals on the
cave wall below. Then ask a friend if they can
guess which animals they are.

Sliding Snakes and Tall Trees

In this fun board game, you have to slide down the snakes and climb up the trees. Who will be first to reach the finish?

You will need:

- Two players
- A die
- Two counters (you can use two different coins)

How to play:

1. Place your counters on START. Throw the die. The player who throws the highest number starts first.

2. Take turns to throw the die and move forward the right number of spaces. But watch out! There are slippery snakes about . . .

   - If you land on the head of a **snake**, you must slide down it and go back to the square where the snake's body ends. Watch out for the owl and the fox too – if you land on one of them, you will also have to go back.

   - But if you land at the bottom of a **tree**, you can climb up it and move your counter to the top.

3. The first player to reach the FINISH square wins. If you've had fun, why not play again?

FINISH

Slide down to number 20

26

25

Fly back with owl to 23

28

27

Follow the fox to number 18

20

21

22

23

24

19

Slide down to number 12

15 Slide down to number 6

18

17

Climb up to number 26

Climb up to number 19

11

16

10

12

13

14

Climb up to number 14

Slide down to number 4

9

8

7

6

5

START

Climb up to number 11

1

2

3

4

23

H is for Home

All kinds of creatures make their homes in woods and forests. Rabbits live in a maze of tunnels called a warren. Badgers dig underground homes called setts. Birds build their nests in the treetops. Do you know where other woodland animals live?

I is for Insect

All insects have six legs and some have wings too, like dragonflies, bees and ladybirds.

A really good place to find insects is under a rotting log. If you look carefully, you will probably find ants and beetles, as well as other creatures such as woodlice, centipedes, slugs, snails and spiders.

J is for Jaws

The Gruffalo has terrible jaws. Animals like foxes and badgers also have strong jaws, for catching smaller animals.

Insects can have tough jaws too. Some tiny beetles can munch their way through a solid tree trunk. Snake jaws can open so wide that a snake can swallow something bigger than its own head!

I'm off

K is for Kingfisher

The blue-headed kingfisher lives near water, where it sits and waits for a juicy fish to swim by. Then – whoosh! The kingfisher does a dramatic dive to catch the fish. It doesn't usually miss!

L is for Ladybird

Has a ladybird ever landed on you? If it has, then you are supposed to be lucky all day.

Ladybirds are tiny beetles with spots on them. Most ladybirds are red with black spots – but there are also yellow and orange ladybirds around. Have you ever seen one?

M is for Moon

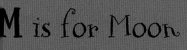

The moon looks so mysterious over the deep dark wood at night …

But have you ever noticed that the moon appears to change shape? Sometimes it looks full and round. At other times, it's a semi-circle or crescent-shaped. This is because as the moon moves around the Earth, different parts of it are lit up. So it doesn't really change shape – it just appears to.

Who's in the Woods?

The mouse meets a fox, an owl, a snake and a Gruffalo in the deep dark wood.
But there are lots of other creatures around that the mouse doesn't see.
Can you match the right names to the pictures?

Frog

Dragonfly

Butterfly

Kingfisher

Deer

Bat

Squirrel

Rabbit

Woodpecker

Beetle

Join the Dots

Which creature is looking at the mouse? Join the dots to find out.
Add whiskers, then colour the picture.

It's Gruffalo Tea Time

**If your tummy's rumbling like the mouse's,
it might be time for some tasty tea time treats …**

"Toowhit Toowhoo" Sandwiches

Make your favourite sandwich and cut two sides off,
just like the picture, so that you have an owl's
body and two wings. Arrange them on a
plate and ask a grown-up to do some
slicing for you. Add cucumber and
carrot slices for eyes. Put raisins
or blueberries in the middle of
the eyes and cut a black olive
for the beak. Make feet out
of pieces of carrot or cheese.
Toowhoo!

What a tasty tweet!

Poisonous Warts

Wash a packet of green grapes,
pull them off their stems and
put them in a bowl.

Gruffalo Eyes

Ask a grown-up to cut circles of
ready sliced cheese. Lay them
on top of round crackers,
with a raisin, olive or half
a grape in the middle.

What big eyes the Gruffalo has!

Sweet Snow Gruffalos

Stick three white marshmallows together
using a tube of white icing. Cut a raisin in
half for the two eyes and glue on with more
icing. Then use red "writing" icing for the
nose. Stick on mini marshmallows
for the arms. Scatter
desiccated coconut around
the Gruffalo for
a snowy effect.

Logpile House

Arrange a packet of cocktail sausages into a pile. Use a jelly snake to decorate.

Crunchy Gruffalo Snack

You will need circular brown crispbreads or rice cakes for the Gruffalo's head. Ask a grown-up to do the slicing and cutting. Use cream cheese to stick on carrot circles and blueberries for the eyes, a green olive for the nose, and sweetcorn teeth. Cut ears and face tusks out of sliced carrot. Finally, cut the tops from two baby sweetcorns for the horns. Serve with extra cheese.

He looks really tasty!

Crispy, crunchy, chewy ...

Chewy marshmallows ... **crispy** crackers ... **crunchy** rice cakes ...
Can you think of other things to eat?

mushy   crackats✓

juicy   tomatos

chewy   mash malo

sticky   sweets

wobbly   Jelly

crunchy   Eucumber

Fantastic Flavours

The Gruffalo likes owl ice cream.
Would *you* like to taste owl ice cream?

Try making up some weird and wonderful
flavours of your own and colour them in.

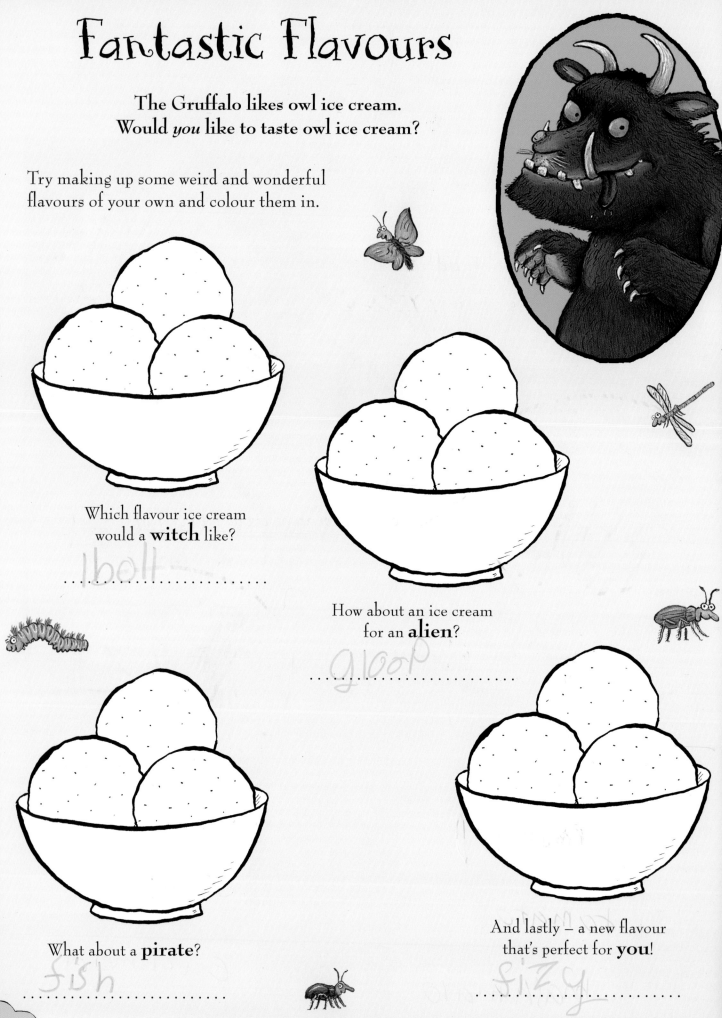

Which flavour ice cream
would a **witch** like?

Ibolt

How about an ice cream
for an **alien**?

gloop

What about a **pirate**?

fish

And lastly – a new flavour
that's perfect for **you**!

fizzy

Terribly Tasty Rhymes

Can you fill in the missing words from the choices below?

"*My favourite food!*" the Gruffalo said.
"*You'll taste good on a slice of* $bread$!"

"You're not the Mouse." "*Toowhoo, not I,*
But he's somewhere nearby, eating gruffalo pie."

"You're not the Mouse." "*Not I,*" said the snake.
"*He's down by the lake – eating gruffalo* $cake$."

All was quiet in the deep dark wood.
The Mouse found a nut and the nut was good.

cake

bread   nut   pie

33

N is for Nut

The mouse loves nibbling on a hazelnut. Squirrels like nuts, too. They usually dig a hole and bury their nuts so that they will have enough food to eat during the winter. When the cold weather comes, the squirrels must remember where they left them.

O is for Owl

If you've ever seen an owl in the wood, you're very lucky. Owls like to hunt at night. They have the most incredible hearing and can detect the tiniest sound of smaller animals, like mice. With their sharp beaks and powerful claws, owls are skilled hunters.

P is for Prickles

The Gruffalo has prickles all over his back. What colour are they?

Prickles can be very useful. Holly leaves have sharp, prickly edges which stop creatures from nibbling them. If a hedgehog is scared, it will roll itself up into a tight ball and make the prickles on its back stand up. Nothing will want to touch it!

the Deep Dark Wood

Q is for Quiet

All was quiet in the deep dark wood …

Woods are usually quiet places. But if you stand still and listen carefully you can hear all sorts of interesting things. Birds chirping, leaves rustling, the wind blowing … If you keep really still, what else might you hear?

R is for Rabbit

Many wild rabbits live in the deep dark wood. Rabbits have very long ears which they use to listen out for predators. If it needs to, a rabbit will thump its back legs on the ground to warn its rabbit friends of any danger.

S is for Snail

You'll always know when a snail has been around because of the slimy trail it leaves behind. The slippery slime protects the snail as it moves along. You will often see snails when it has been raining. They come up above the rain-soaked soil so they can breathe properly.

T is for Tree

Many different trees grow in the woods. The tall tree on this page is called the silver birch because of its lovely silvery-white trunk. Next to it is a pine tree, which has needle-shaped leaves.

Can you name any other trees that you know?

What a Noise!

It's very noisy in the deep dark wood today.

Which animals are making these sounds? Make the sound and point to the animal.

Fill in the empty bubble with another woodland sound.

Colour by Numbers

Use the guide to colour the picture.

1 Blue	**2** Green	**3** Orange	
4 Brown	**5** Grey	**6** Pink	

Mouse Mirth

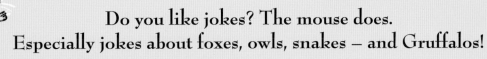

Do you like jokes? The mouse does.
Especially jokes about foxes, owls, snakes – and Gruffalos!

Why did the owl 'owl?

Because the woodpecker wood peck 'er!

What do you call an owl with a low voice?

A growl.

What happened when the owl lost its voice?

It didn't give a hoot!

Which hand do you use to pick up a dangerous snake?

Someone else's!

What kind of snake is good at maths?

An adder.

Hee hee!

Why did the fox say "Moo"?

It was learning a foreign language.

If a fox jumped into the stream, what's the first thing it would do?

Get wet!

What has terrible tusks, terrible claws and goes up and down?

A Gruffalo in a lift.

What should you do if you find a Gruffalo in your bed?

Sleep in the wardrobe.

Acting the Gruffalo
by Julia Donaldson

When I was a little girl, I wanted to be an actress, and my sister Mary and I were always putting on shows. We liked to get the whole family involved. I remember once I wrote a play of *Little Red Riding Hood*. My father had the part of the woodcutter, but he wouldn't take it seriously and kept getting the giggles, which made me very cross!

Mary and me at a fancy dress competition. I'm the bucket and she's the spade.

This is my family and me on the steps of our house.
Front row: my sister Mary, my friend (also Mary!), and me
Middle row: my mother, Auntie Beta
Back row: my father, Auntie Mary

When I grew up, I still loved performing just as much. I always enjoyed writing songs as well as plays. Here I am singing as a student, with my husband Malcolm playing the guitar.

Here I am playing the part of Lola the Kitchen Cat in my musical, *King Grunt's Cake* which I wrote when I was about 25 years old. I would never have guessed then that one day one of my most popular parts would be as a mouse!

I never became a full-time actor, but nowadays Malcolm and I are often on stage performing my own songs and picture book stories. Here we are, practising being the fox and the mouse.

Performing *The Gruffalo* on stage

Why don't you try putting on your own show of *The Gruffalo*? You could make some masks for the different creatures. Have plenty of practice before you perform to an audience, though: it's important to learn your lines and work out where everyone is going to be on the stage. And remember, do try not to get the giggles!

Odd One Out

The mouse has been busy making lots of snow Gruffalos. But one is different from all the others. Can you find it?

Answers on page 61!

What's in the Snow?

Aha! Oho! What has the Gruffalo's Child spotted in the snow? A creature? A footprint? A plant, an insect — or something else?

Draw whatever you think the Gruffalo's Child is looking at, then colour in your picture.

Make an Owl

Would you like to make an owl like the one in *The Gruffalo*?
Here's how!

You will need:

- two paper plates
- an egg box
- cotton wool balls
- glue or sticky tape
- scissors, ruler and pencil
- thread or string
- poster or acrylic paint: brown, orange, yellow, black and white
- a grown-up helper

! Ask a grown up to help with the tricky cutting.

1. Use your ruler to draw two lines on the back of a plate, as in the picture above.

2. Cut along the lines so that you have three pieces of plate. The middle piece will be the owl's body; the other two pieces its wings. Glue or tape the wings to the body, so that the pieces fit together as the picture shows.

3. Trim the end of the body to make a more rounded shape.

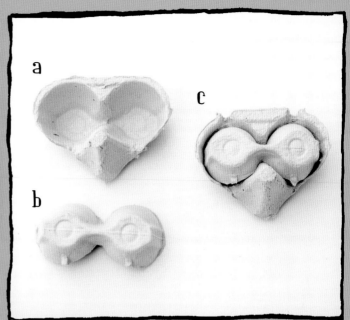

a

c

b

6. Here's the face and beak (a). Cut out a second pair of egg hollows to make its eyes (b). Trim around the sides so that you can fit them into the owl's face (c).

4. Paint the wings brown and let them dry.

5. Now take your egg box and cut out a piece like this, for the owl's face and beak.

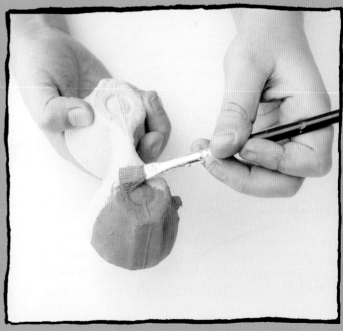

7. Paint the eyes orange and the face and beak black. When the eyes are dry, paint black circles in the middle.

45

8. Use sticky tape to stick the head on to the body.

9. Glue cotton wool balls all over the body and on to the top and sides of the head.

11. Add little strokes of white paint to the wings for the owl's markings. Mix black and white paint together to make grey and add markings on to the cotton wool body.

12. When your owl is finished, stick some thread or string behind the head with tape Then you can tie it or stick it to the wall or ceiling. *"Toowhit Toowhoo!"*

10. To make the feet, cut two small pieces from the edge of the second paper plate. Draw three little triangles on the end of the feet and cut them out. Paint the feet yellow and, when they are dry, stick them on to the body with tape.

Body Bits Crossword

Use the picture clues to complete the crossword. All the words are parts of animals' bodies. Some letters have already been filled in to help you.

1

2

3

4

5 across

5 down

6

7

8

9

Answers on page 61!

Crossword letters filled in:
³W O r t
²B
⁴e a r s
e
k
¹N O S e
⁵T u s k
E
E
⁶e y
⁸T a i l
⁷C t a
H
⁹W i n g
s

U is for Underground House

Foxes live in underground places called dens. A den might be a hole dug into the ground or a burrow underneath a garden shed. Foxes like cosy, sheltered homes and will make their dens in all kinds of places.

V is for Viper

The snake in *The Gruffalo* is a viper (also known as an adder). The viper has black markings down its body and a black tongue.

It is the only poisonous snake in Great Britain, so if you should ever see one, be careful! However, it will probably be much more scared of you and will quickly slither away.

W is for Whiskers

Lots of creatures have whiskers. But what are they for? Whiskers help animals to feel things and to find things. Some animals, like moles, use their sensitive whiskers to find their way around in the dark. Can you think of other animals that have whiskers?

the Deep Dark Wood

X is in Fox

We know that foxes live in woods but they can also live in towns and cities. Perhaps you've seen one? They are usually easy to spot with their orange-red fur, pointed ears and thick tails, which are called brushes.

Y is for Yellow

Colourful wild flowers grow in the deep dark wood. The brightest of all are the yellow flowers: daffodils, buttercups, dandelions and cowslips. A buttercup is so bright and shiny that you can see its yellow reflection if you hold it under your chin.

Z is in Buzz

In the wood you'll often hear the buzzing of a bee, fly or wasp. These insects make a buzzing sound by beating their wings very, very fast, usually when they are flying. Bees also buzz when they have landed on a flower, as they are trying to shake the pollen from the flower on to their body.

A Cosy Home

Fox lives in an underground house.

Where would *you* like to live?
What would you put in there?
Draw your ideal home.

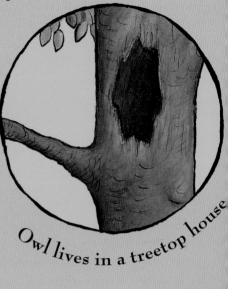

Owl lives in a treetop house

Snake lives in a logpile house.

I carry my home around with me!

The Gruffalo lives in a cave.

The Name Game

Play this game with a friend or a grown-up.

How to Play

- Player 1 thinks of an animal and tells Player 2 a fact about it.

- Player 2 has to guess what the animal is.

- If he/she is wrong, Player 1 thinks of another fact about that animal and Player 2 guesses again.

- If that's still not correct, Player 1 tells Player 2 a third fact about the animal.

Guessing the answer after the first fact wins 3 points.

Guessing the answer after the second fact wins 2 points.

Guessing the answer after the third fact wins 1 point.

If Player 2 still hasn't guessed the answer after the third fact then he/she gets 0 points.

Here are some examples to start you off:

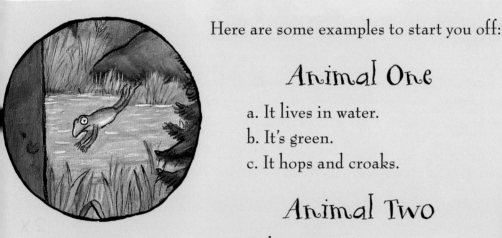

Animal One

a. It lives in water.
b. It's green.
c. It hops and croaks.

Animal Two

a. It has wings.
b. It's an insect.
c. There are lovely colours on its wings.

Animal Three

a. It lives in caves.
b. It has wings.
c. It likes to hang upside down.

Animal Four

a. It likes being in trees.
b. It eats nuts.
c. It has a bushy tail.

Now think of some more animals and play again!

"It's Owl," *said the mouse.* "Why, Owl, hello!"
Owl took one look at the Gruffalo.
"Oh dear!" *he said.* "Goodbye, little mouse,"
And off he flew to his treetop house.

Difference

Look at the two pictures carefully.
Can you find six differences between them?

Answers on page 61!

Great Gruffalo Games

Would you like to be a Gruffalo? Well, now you can!
Just play our first great Gruffalo game – then try the others.

Squeak Mouse Squeak!

For four players or more

You will need:
- Blindfold or scarf

Everyone sits in a circle. One person is blindfolded and becomes the Gruffalo. The Gruffalo has to look for the mouse.

A grown-up leads the Gruffalo around the circle until the Gruffalo says "Stop". Then the Gruffalo kneels down in front of the nearest player (now called the mouse) and says, "Squeak, Mouse, squeak!"

The mouse makes a high squeaking noise and the Gruffalo has to guess who it is. If the Gruffalo is right, they change places. The mouse becomes blindfolded and is now the Gruffalo. If not, the Gruffalo goes around the circle again and keeps trying different "mice".

Mouse Hunt

For three players or more

You will need:
- Paper and pencil

Tear the paper up into ten pieces and draw a little picture of a mouse on each piece. Send the other players out, then hide the paper mice around the room.

The players now come back inside. They have to find the mice – while behaving like a Gruffalo! They can stomp around saying things like: *"I'm the scariest creature in this wood!" "Where are you, little mouse?" "I'm hungry!"*
The Gruffalo who finds the most mice is the winner.

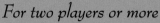

The Gruffalo Says . . .

For two players or more

This is like the game "Simon Says...". A grown-up leads the game.
When he/she says:

- **The Gruffalo says, be a mouse!** everyone squeaks.
- **The Gruffalo says, be a snake!** everyone hisses and makes snake movements with their arms.
- **The Gruffalo says, be an owl!** everyone flaps both arms.
- **The Gruffalo says, be a Gruffalo!** everyone makes tusks on their head with their fingers, and growls.

BUT if the grown-up says, for example, **Be a mouse!** without first saying **The Gruffalo says...** then the players should do nothing. Anyone who accidentally does the animal action or sound is out of the game. The last person left is the winner.

The Gruffalo's Child Doodle Game

For two players or more

You will need:

- Pens/pencils
- Sheets of paper

Each player draws a line, a squiggle or a shape very quickly on a piece of paper. The players exchange papers and have one minute to make a funny drawing out of the other person's shape or line. When they've finished, they compare their pictures. There are no winners – it's just fun to do!

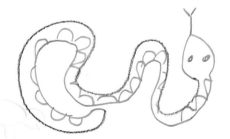

What Comes Next?

Draw what you think the next picture should be.

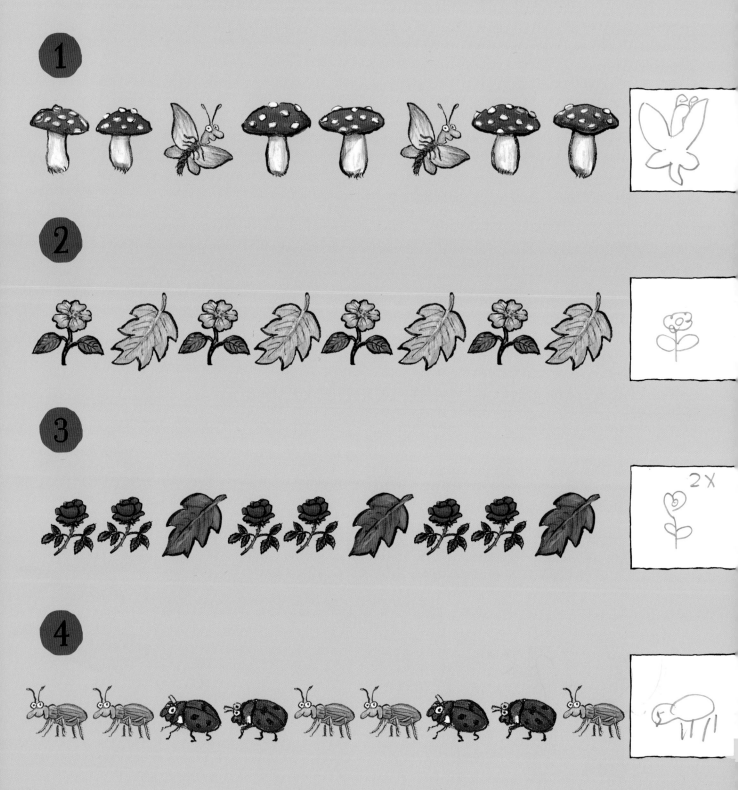

1

2

3

4

Answers on page 6[

Are you a Gruffalo Genius?

How much do you know about the characters in the Gruffalo books?
Try this fun quiz and find out.

1 **What colour is the Gruffalo's tongue?**
- **a.** Black ☐
- **b.** Green ☐
- **c.** Purple ☐

2 **Which of these creatures has whiskers?**
- **a.** The fox ☐
- **b.** The owl ☐
- **c.** The snake ☐

3 **The mouse says that the Gruffalo likes owl …**
- **a.** Pie ☐
- **b.** Crumble ☐
- **c.** Ice cream ☐

4 **The snake invites the mouse to his logpile house for a …**
- **a.** Party ☐
- **b.** Feast ☐
- **c.** Cup of tea ☐

5 **What noise does the Gruffalo make when he's sleeping?**
a. He shouts ☐
b. He snores ☐
c. He coughs ☐

6 **Which creature in the deep dark wood says "Too whoo"!**
a. The snake ☐
b. The mouse ☐
c. The owl ☐

7 **The Gruffalo is covered in …**
a. Scales ☐
b. Fur ☐
c. Feathers ☐

8 **The Gruffalo says that the Big Bad Mouse has eyes like "pools of terrible … "?**
a. Mud ☐
b. Fire ☐
c. Water ☐

9 What is the weather like when the Gruffalo's Child goes looking for the Big Bad Mouse?

a. Sunny ☐

b. Snowy ☐

c. Rainy ☐

10 What is the mouse doing when the Gruffalo's Child finds him?

a. Sweeping with a broom ☐

b. Washing clothes ☐

c. Eating a nut ☐

Answers on page 61!

Now count the number of questions you got right.

7-10
Gruffalo Genius!

You've certainly read the Gruffalo books lots of times! Is there anything you don't know about the Gruffalo? What a star!

4-6
Good work, Gruffalo!

Well done. You know your Gruffalo stuff. Give yourself a big Gruffalo pat on the back!

0-3
Go again, Gruffalo!

You can't remember everything about the Gruffalo but that doesn't matter. Just read the stories again and you're sure to get more answers right next time!

A Gruffalo Goodbye

It's time to leave the deep dark wood.
Fill in the missing letters, then draw lines to match the animals to their names.

Sn_ke

The Gruffalo's Ch_ld

F_x

_ouse

Goodbye! See you next time.

Ow_

The Gruffal_

Answers

Page 12: A Walk in the Woods

There are ten logs in the logpile house.
The footprints belong to a Gruffalo.
There are eight pine cones on the path.

Page 16: Snowy Tracks

a: mouse tracks b: fox tracks c: owl tracks
d: snake trail

Page 20: Animal Art

1: mouse 2: snake 3: owl 4: fox

Page 26: Who's in the Woods?

1: Bat 2: Woodpecker 3: Beetle 4: Squirrel
5: Deer 6: Frog 7: Dragonfly 8: Rabbit
9: Butterfly 10: Kingfisher

Page 33: Terribly Tasty Rhymes

The answers in order are bread, pie, cake and
nut (twice).

Pages 36: What a Noise!

The mouse – "Squeak!"
The woodpecker – "Tap tap tap!"
The owl – "Toowhit toowhoo!"
The bird – "Tweet tweet!"
The snake – "Hisssss!"
The frog – "Croak!"

Page 42: Odd One Out

Snow Gruffalo 'e' is missing its twig toes.

Page 47: Body Bits Crossword

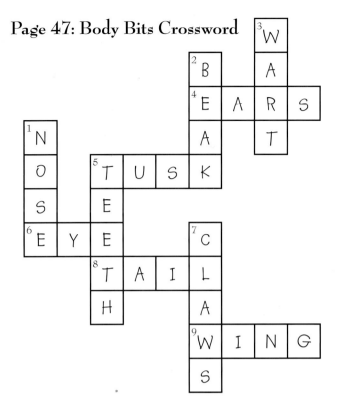

Pages 52: Spot the Difference

Page 56: What Comes Next?

1: Butterfly 2: Blue flower 3: Red rose
4: Beetle

Pages 57: Are you a Gruffalo Genius?

1: a, 2: a, 3: c, 4: b, 5: b, 6: c, 7: b, 8: b,
9: b, 10: a

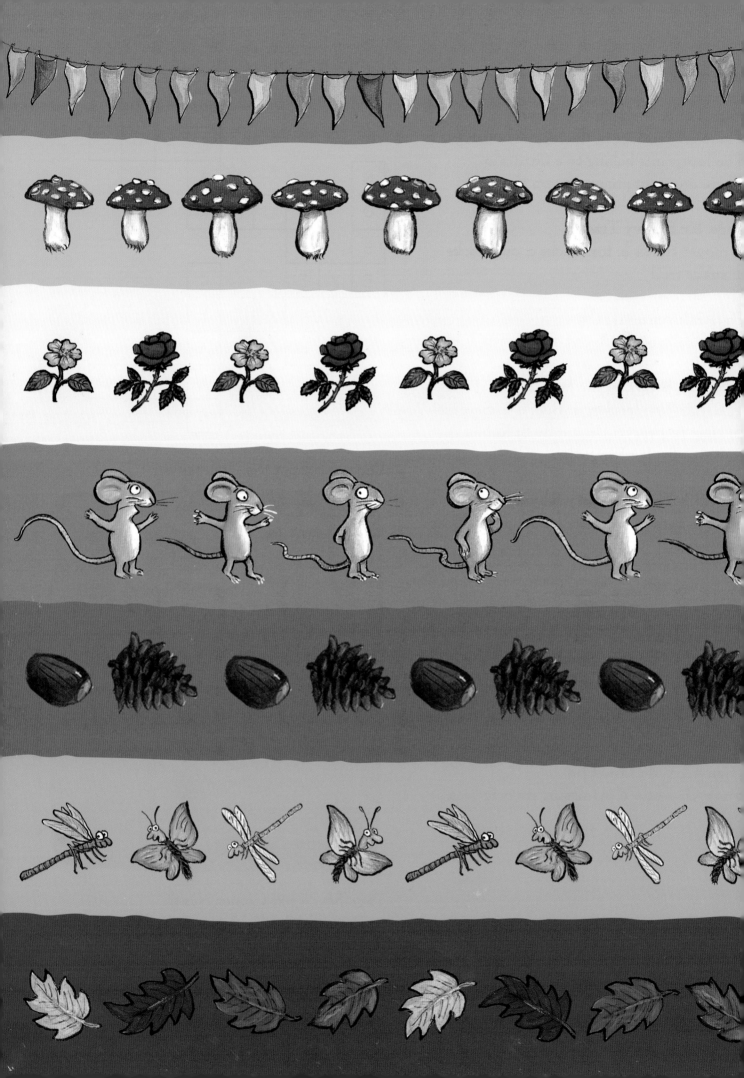